# Reading Basics

## An Early Reader Series

## Book 5

Annie Brown and
Alpha Omega Staff

Illustrated by Samar Waterworth
and Alpha Omega Staff

Alpha Omega Publications
300 North McKemy Avenue
Chandler, Arizona 85226-2618

ALPHA
OMEGA
PUBLICATIONS INC.

# Instant Words

|      |      |       |        |         |
|------|------|-------|--------|---------|
| 1.   | the  | he    | go     | who     |
| 2.   | a    | I     | see    | an      |
| 3.   | is   | they  | then   | their   |
| 4.   | you  | one   | us     | she     |
| 5.   | to   | good  | no     | new     |
| 6.   | and  | me    | him    | said    |
| 7.   | we   | about | by     | did     |
| 8.   | that | had   | was    | boy     |
| 9.   | in   | if    | come   | three   |
| 10.  | not  | some  | get    | down    |
| 11.  | for  | up    | or     | work    |
| 12.  | at   | her   | two    | put     |
| 13.  | with | do    | man    | were    |
| 14.  | it   | when  | little | before  |
| 15.  | on   | so    | has    | just    |
| 16.  | can  | my    | them   | long    |
| 17.  | will | very  | how    | here    |
| 18.  | are  | all   | like   | other   |

# Instant Words

| 19. | of | would | our | old |
|-----|-----|-------|-----|-----|
| 20. | this | any | what | take |
| 21. | your | been | know | cat |
| 22. | as | out | make | again |
| 23. | but | there | which | give |
| 24. | be | from | much | after |
| 25. | have | day | his | many |
| 26. | could | behind | launch | wear |
| 27. | animals | across | directions | dolphin |
| 28. | water | build | laugh | |

# Bobo, The Clown

Bobo is a funny clown.

He knows how to make us laugh.

Bobo's coat is long and red.

His big hat is yellow.

He has funny, long shoes on his feet.

Bobo's car is little and old.

He goes around and around.

His car has

balloons on it.

We like to go to

Bobo's show.

We think he's

very funny.

# Thank You, God

From my window I can see,
So many things God made for me.

The yellow sun and morning light,
The moon and stars in the dark
of night.

Grass and flowers, hills and trees,
Butterflies and little bees.

Rain, waterfalls, and birds
that fly, white clouds and a
rainbow in the sky.
For all these things we must say,
"Thank you, God," every day.

# Building a Town

Toby had a new dump truck. Tony had a new road grader.

"Let's build a town," said Toby. "We could use our toys to build houses and stores."

"Yes," said Tony, "we could build long roads all around our town."

The boys worked hard. They used their toys to build roads and buildings.

Toby and Tony played with their town for a long time. It was fun.

# The Pony Show

"Oh, Mother," said Pam. "There's going to be a Pony Show. Please may I take JoJo to the show?"

Pam's mother said she could. So the next morning Pam took JoJo to the Pony Show.

Many ponies were there. The children rode their ponies around in a circle. Around and around they went, one pony behind the other.

JoJo didn't get a prize, but Pam and her pony had a good time at the Pony Show.

# Old, Old Goat

Down the road went an old, old goat.
He stopped and looked.
There by the road was a blue boat.
Old, old goat took a bite.
No, no! Boats are not good to eat.
Down the road he went.

Old, old goat stopped again.
There by the road was a red coat.

Old, old goat took a bite.
No, no! Coats are not good to eat.
Down the road he went.

Old, old goat stopped again.
There by the road was some green grass.
Old, old goat took a bite.
Oh, oh! The grass was good.

Old, old goat began to eat.
Green grass is good to eat.

# Animals

There are many kinds of animals.

Some animals are very little.

Some are very big.

Some animals can fly.

Many animals have hair or fur.

Some animals have four feet, some animals have two feet, and some have no feet at all.

Many animals sleep when it is very cold.
Some animals work for us.

We have some animals for pets.
We can play with them.
Some animals cannot be pets.
They are wild.

# Building Rockets

The children at Joel's school are building rockets. They have kits with all the rocket parts in them. They read the directions. Then they put the rockets together. Mr. Jones will help them launch their rockets behind their school.

Ready!

10
9
8
7
6
5
4
3
2
1

Blast-Off!

# Joseph's Dream

What a dream!
I saw my brothers'
grain bowing to my grain!
I saw the sun and the
moon and the eleven stars
bowing down to me.
Wow!

# Clouds

Clouds are like sailing ships.
They sail across the sky.
They sail in one day, and then they go...
   I wish I could tell why.

Clouds are like sailing ships.
They sail across the sky.
One day I'll sail away with them...
   Then I will tell you why.

# Dolphin

Dolphin, think what fun it might be
If you lived on the land,
And I lived in the sea.

You might take a ride on my new sled.
I might sleep in your water bed.

Dolphin, think what fun it might be
If you lived on the land,
And I lived in the sea.

# My Father and Mother

My mother and father help me.

They fix good meals for my brother and me.

We laugh and talk at the table.

They want to know about my day.

I tell them funny stories.

Even my brother laughs at the stories.

My mother and father take good care of us.
They buy clothes for us to wear.
Sometimes I have to wait for the things
I want.
But I always have the things I need.
I love my mother and father very much.
My brother and I kiss them and tell them
that we love them.

# The Wait

The toys wait.
Will the boy come to play today?
Will his sis come, too?
They will wait for him.
He will play with them.
When he has a choice, he will
come to play.
Will it be today?

# Snoopers

Snoopers is Mr. Jordan's dog. He is a basset hound. His body is low to the ground and his ears are long and droopy. Snoopers is slow and doesn't have very good eyesight or hearing, but he has a nose that can sniff out anything. He got his name because he is the best sniffer in town.

18

Mr. Jordan's home is behind his feed store on the corner of Mill and First Street. Snoopers spends most of his time at the feed store. In his younger years it was free of critters and pests. Snooper sniffed out any mouse, rabbit, or other pest that tried to get a nibble of the feed Mr. Jordan sold to farmers. He let out a loud howl to alert his owner and the intruder would be chased away.

Today, Snoopers still spends most of his time at the feed store. His old body is slower and his long ears are so droopy they drag on the ground. He lays on the front porch for much of the day. He's done his work. Every once in awhile he'll raise his nose and sniff. The critters know he still has the best sniffer in town.

Yes, Snoopers can still sniff out any mouse, rabbit or pest that crosses his path.

Maybe that's why those critters are using the back door these days.

Drawing by:
Nathan Smith

# My Gift

Today is the big art show. I am not a very good artist, but Nathan can draw anything. He will win first prize, I'm sure.

My teacher said we don't have to be a great artist. She just wants us to do our best. Mom and Dad say that, too. "Do your best," they will say. I've heard it since I was a young boy.

Our pastor says we all have different gifts. They are special gifts the Lord has given to each of us. I think God gave Nathan a gift to draw. I don't know what my gift is yet, but I can't wait to find out. Mom says it might be the way I make people feel good about themselves.

I can't wait for the art show today. I will tell Nathan he is a great artist and I think his drawing of the red-tail hawk is awesome. I will tell him he should win first prize.

I hope Nathan will feel good today. I hope I will make him smile.

# The Gold Coin

Joy and Howie were playing in the sandbox when Howie jumped up and shouted, "Look what I found!"

The other children came quickly to see what the excitement was all about.

Howie opened his hand and showed them the shiny, gold coin he found while digging a deep tunnel in the sand. It wasn't like any other coin he had seen.

"Wow!" Joy said.

"What are you going to do with that cool coin?" a red-headed boy asked.

"I'm going to put it in a jar and set it on my dresser," answered Howie.

"I think you should make a sign to ask if someone lost it," said Joy. The others agreed.

Howie thought about it for a few minutes.

"You're right, Joy. If I lost this coin, I would be happy if someone found it and gave it back to me," Howie told her.

Joy smiled at her friend. Then they ran to Howie's house to get paper and crayons. Joy and Howie spent the rest of the afternoon making signs.

When the signs were finished they went back to the park and taped them to the light posts and benches.

Howie took the shiny, gold coin home and put it in a jar on his dresser.

"I can look at it every day," he thought to himself. He knew he might not get to keep the coin for long, but he would still take very good care of it.

# Playmates of the Sea

Have you ever seen a person ride on the back of a dolphin? It can happen! Dolphins are gentle, playful animals who enjoy being around people. They love to be petted or stroked on their rubbery skin.

Bottlenose dolphins are the most common to us. They are used in sea park shows and television programs like "Flipper." If you look at them closely, it looks like they are always smiling.

Many people don't know this, but dolphins are really small whales. They are mammals like dogs, cows and you.

Dolphins live mostly underwater but do not have gills like fish. Because they are mammals they have to come to the surface every few minutes to get a breath of air.

There are over thirty-nine kinds of dolphins. They come in many shapes, sizes and colors.

Dolphins have large brains and are very smart. It is easy for trainers to work with them and teach them tricks. They have good memories, too. Dolphins can often be spotted doing their own tricks in the ocean waters. Some can jump, twist or spin. They may even do back flips.

Dolphins have fantastic hearing. Their ears are very small holes on the sides of their head but can pick up sounds from miles away. They "see" with their ears as they swim about the ocean. Because they are so smart and have this great sense of hearing, dolphins have been very useful to people.

If you ever take a ride out in a boat, you may see a herd of dolphins. Most live together in large groups. There may be thousands in one herd. If you see a herd of dolphins or visit a sea park where they have trained dolphins, ask one to play. It may nod its head, saying, "Yes, yes!"

# Nurse Jane

Life can be pretty tough on the
   playground.

Just take a day like today.

Ted and Randy bumped into a tree,
Alice Freemon scraped her knee.
Roger Orbin got stung by a bee.

It was a tough day for these three.

Lucky for them there is Nurse Jane.

Charles and Sherman got sand in their
   eyes.
Ellen and Trisha ate their mud pies.
Sandy Plunket started to cry.
I guess she got blisters when she climbed
   too high.

Lucky for them there is Nurse Jane.

Nurse Jane sees their scrapes and cleans
   off the dirt.
She puts ice on their bumps and fixes
   ripped shirts.

Nurse Jane checks the boys' eyes for
   small specks of sand.
She puts ointment and band-aids on
   Sandy's sore hands.

Nurse Jane doesn't scold us or even get
   mad.
She even understands our feelings when
   we are sad.

Nurse Jane is the nurse who can change
   a bad day,
As she cares for our hurts and sends us
   back out to play.

Life can be pretty tough on the
playground.

Unless you're lucky enough to have a
nurse like Nurse Jane.

# Tornado

A tornado is a powerful wind funnel. It begins in the clouds of a strong thunderstorm. A tornado can happen anywhere in the world. Most tornadoes happen in an area of the United States called "Tornado Alley." The worst months for tornadoes are April, May and June.

A tornado is all air, but it isn't invisible. This is because it picks up dirt, grass, leaves and all kinds of trash that are in its path. It looks like a giant black finger as it comes down from the clouds.

A tornado can move very fast or spin in one place. Its powerful winds howl and scream. It roars like a fast-moving train.

The tornado twists and turns back and

forth, looping here and there as it makes a path on the ground. Sometimes we call tornadoes "twisters" because of the way they move.

The force of a tornado is so strong it destroys everything in its path. As the twister zips by, buildings rattle and shake. If the building is in its path, it will become a pile of rubble. Most tornadoes last only a few minutes, but they do a lot of damage in that short time.

Tornadoes are dangerous. They have destroyed whole towns and killed animals and people. If you ever see a tornado, don't take time to watch it. You never know what direction it will go. Get to a safe place, fast!

# God is our Rock

Larson knelt down and picked up a
small rock in Trevor Morton's front yard.

The rocks, broken glass and pieces of wood were all that was left of the Morton's house.

Last night a tornado had whirled down their street. It knocked down trees, fences and anything else in its path. Trash was everywhere.

Larson looked at the rock for awhile. He remembered the verse his Sunday School teacher had taught last week. "The Lord is my Rock. That means He gives us strength when we face hard times," she had said to the class.

In the kitchen he heard his mother talking. "This is going to be a hard time for all of us," she said. "But it will be hardest for the Mortons. We will all need to be strong."

"I must do something to help them," Larson thought. "What can I do? I'm just a small boy. I can't clean up all the mess myself."

He looked at the rock again and held it tight. Then he remembered what his parents did when they needed an answer. He closed his eyes and prayed to God. When he finished praying he put the rock in his pocket.

Later that day other children from his classroom were talking about ways they could help the Mortons. They were the lucky ones. Their homes were okay. When they finished talking they had a plan.

They would work in teams to clean up the trash and then have a car wash to make money to help Trevor's family buy new things. They would work hard. They would work together.

Larson knew God was his Rock and gave him strength in times that are hard. He knew God heard his prayer and answered it. He wanted to be sure Trevor knew how great God is, too.

Before school was out, Larson reached in his pocket and pulled out the rock he had found in Trevor's yard. He wrote on it, "The Lord is my Rock" and then gave it to Trevor.

# The Old Red Barn

The old red barn sat in the same place for over fifty years. Farmer Anders and his wife had built it themselves. One by one they nailed each piece of wood to make sides that stood ten feet tall. They put rails up inside the barn so the animals would have a place to sleep at night. Then it was time to put on the roof. Mrs. Anders remembered it being the hardest part.

I didn't like climbing that ol' ladder," she would tell her friends. "I still don't."

When the building was done they painted it bright red. "It took twenty-two gallons of red paint," Farmer Anders would tell folks.

44

"It looks like a ripe tomato, only square," some folks would say.

That old red barn was home to Sally Sue, the sweet, gray spotted horse; Mr. Smooze, the rowdy ram;, and Betsy Boo, the milk cow. The chickens and turkeys were penned in a yard that went around the side of the barn. It was their home, too.

But the city was growing and the freeway would be coming their way. The people from the city told the Anders that the old red barn, which they had built themselves, and their house would have to come down. The buildings were right in the path of the new freeway.

It was a sad time for the Anders. They couldn't tell the city people to find a different path for the freeway. Moving was their only choice. Friends came by. They cried a little and told stories about growing up around the old red barn. Homes were found for Sally Sue, Mr. Smooze, Betsy Boo, and the chickens and turkeys.

As for Farmer Anders and his wife, they packed up the boxes and moved to a small house in town. It was nice, but they missed their old red barn.

One day friends came by with boards from the old red barn. One by one they nailed them together at the front of the house.

From that day on the Anders sat on their new red porch each night. They told stories about their years on the farm with

the old red barn. But they didn't miss it
anymore.

# Cory's Kitten

Cory raced home from school on her bike.

"Mom, can I go down to the corner market?" she asked as she ran in the house.

"Again?" her mother asked. "You've been going there every day this week."

"I just want to see the kittens," Cory replied.

"Okay, but don't be long," Mom told her.

Cory hopped on her bike and headed for the corner market. "I can't wait to see how much they've grown today!"

Cory parked her bike near the market's back door and quietly walked toward the shed. There they were, all seven, snuggled up in a cozy box with their mother, Darby.

The kittens were just 4 days old. Two were male and five were female. All of them were gray, except for one of the little girls. She was black with blue eyes. Cory loved them all, but the little black one was her favorite.

Cory checked on the kittens every day for the next five weeks. She would give them treats and play with them for hours. "If only I could take one home," she told Mrs. Thurston, the market owner.

Finally, it was time for the kittens to have their own home.

"Let's go look at those kittens," Dad said to Cory.

Cory couldn't believe it. "Really?" she asked. She had hoped her parents would let her have a kitten, but she hadn't been brave enough to ask just yet.

"Mrs. Thurston told us how well you have taken care of the kittens these past few weeks. We thought you might like to have one of your very own," Dad told her.

Cory beamed. "This is the best day ever!" she exclaimed. Of course, she knew which one she would choose.

54

# The Kitten Gets a Name

Cory was so excited about her new kitten. As soon as school was over she ran across the street to show Mr. and Mrs. Morton. "She's darling," Mrs. Morton said.

Then she called her best friends, Clark and Julie. "Come over and see my new kitten," she told them.

"She's so soft," Julie told her as she held the kitten gently.

"What's her name?" Clark asked, teasing her with a string.

"That's the problem," Cory replied. "I can't decide."

"How about Blackie?" Julie asked.

"Maybe," replied Cory. But she thought Blackie was a boring name.

That night Dad told Cory to watch the kitten closely. "When I was a boy I named my dog "Tag" because he liked to play the game. Maybe the kitten will do something to help you think of a name."

The next morning Cory wasn't any closer to choosing a name. "All she does is follow me everywhere," she told her mom and dad.

"Hmmmm," said Dad. "That gives me an idea."

Dad took Cory outside. It was a sunny day and just right for showing her his idea.

"Okay," he said. "I want you to walk around on the driveway. Now look on the ground. What do you see following you everywhere you go?"

"I see my shadow!" Cory cried out. "I get it! My shadow is black and my kitten is black. My shadow follows me and my kitten follows me."

"Well, now what do you think?" Dad asked, smiling at Cory.

"I think Shadow is a perfect name for my kitten!" she shouted.

"Shadow, where are youuuuuuu...?" Cory called as she went back in the house.

"She's right behind you, of course,"
laughed Mom and Dad.

# Little Garden

Little Garden, little garden,
what will you grow for me?

I use my hands to loosen the soil.
What will you grow for me?

I plant the seeds in the perfect rows.
What will you grow for me?

I water the ground so the roots can drink.
What will you grow for me?

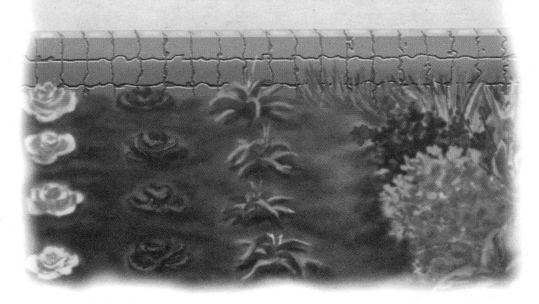

I give you shade from the hot summer sun.
What will you grow for me?

Little garden, little garden,
I see the sprouts popping through the
ground, the tender stems and tiny leaves.
They reach up for the bright blue sky.
I see the brand new life.

Little garden, little garden, it doesn't
matter what you grow for me, or what
these seeds will be.
Only that I care for them the best that I
know how.

The rest I'll wait and see.